Dirty Monkeys Smell Bad

Written and Illustrated by G. Katz Chronicle

Publisher: IMNF Education Press

Cover Design: G. Katz Chronicle
Copyright 2018
First edition

Special thanks to Sabrina Kee
for all of her technical and creative assistance.

"One-thousand-eight-hundered-
eight divided by twenty-two!?!
What do I do?
What do I do?"

1

"**D**irty **M**onkeys **S**mell **B**ad," said a voice offering a strange clue. A puzzled look made the voice repeat, "**D**irty **M**onkeys **S**mell **B**ad." Nothing new.

The voice went on.
My friend,
        seeing my numbness —
I listened, intent on
        disguising my dumbness.

"'**D**' for **D**irty also stands for **D**ivide — this time not as easy, perhaps, as others you've tried.

Ten divided by two is five, you know. You memorized five times two long ago. You know seventy-two divided by eight, easy as pie. The answer must be nine because the opposite of division is to multiply."

"Times tables in the thousands —
no one remembers.
Can't do it by June or
six more Septembers!"

"**D**irty **M**onkeys **S**mell
Bad," was his reply.

4

Continuing to listen,
    I let out a sigh.

"You know your times tables?"

No Nodding, I responded, proud
    of at least THAT I was able.

"And since you know five
times two is ten, you must
also know ten divided by
two — I needn't go over
that again?"

"The answer is five.
    Five of course.

But from this
how do we
arrive at the
answer to my
problem? I fear
I'm growing
hoarse!"

5

"**D**irty **M**onkeys **S**mell **B**ad — let me finish!
'**D**' for **D**irty also stands for **D**ivide.

In division there are basic rules
by which we must abide."

6

At that he took out a clothespin
and attached it to his nose.
Apparently to illustrate
that without my
morning shower I didn't
smell like a rose.

Guided to the sink
and to the soap,
continuing to listen
for help with division
was my only hope.

7

$$22 \overline{)1808}$$

"Let's look at this twenty-two," he said,
"We must divide it into
one-thousand-eight-hundred-eight.
Use your head."

Washing and thinking,
   I was at a loss.
      Didn't know which —
the soap
      or the math —
I wanted to toss.

"Take it step by step," he suggested. "By the end of the week we're going to be tested.

$$22 \overline{)1808}$$

Look at that twenty-two. Could it fit into the one or the eighteen? You know it can't as well as I do.

$$22 \overline{)1808}$$

Try the one-hundred-eighty now. How many times can twenty-two fit into one-hundered-eighty. How many will it allow?

Seven perhaps? Try it and see.
<u>In division scrap paper is mandatory.</u>

Nope. Not seven.
Nine perhaps?
It can't be eleven!

$$\begin{array}{r} {}^{1}22 \\ \times\ 7 \\ \hline 154 \end{array}$$

$$\begin{array}{r} {}^{1}22 \\ \times\ 9 \\ \hline 198 \end{array}$$

Nope. Nine's too big.
Eight seems logical.
Long division is truely
DIABOLICAL!"

$$22\overline{)1808}^{8}$$

"The 'D' is done.
What next for
Dirty Monkeys Smell Bad?" I said.

"Multiply, of course, 'M' for **M**onkey and **M**ultiply."

He handed me a towel with which to dry.

$$\begin{array}{r} 8 \\ {}^1 22\overline{)1808} \\ 6 \end{array}$$

"Eight times two is sixteen.

Eight times two is sixteen plus one is seventeen."

$$\begin{array}{r} 8 \\ {}^1 22\overline{)1808} \\ 176 \end{array}$$

"What's next?
Enough of Dirty Monkeys
I have seen!"

He removed the clothespin,
happy to see
a once dirty monkey
now clean.

$$22\overline{)1808}$$
$$\,8$$
$$-176$$
$$\ \ \ 4$$

"'**S**' stands for
Subtract as well
as **S**mell.
Remember
these
steps
and in division
you'll do well."

Subtract I did
and when I was through
I asked what's next,
"What's next to do?"

"'**B**' stands for **B**ad as well as
Bring Down.
If the problems' not done
you must again go around."

$$22\overline{)1808}$$
$$\begin{array}{r} 8 \\ 22\overline{)1808} \\ -176 \\ \hline 4 \end{array}$$

$$\begin{array}{r} 8 \\ 22\overline{)1808} \\ -176\downarrow \\ \hline 48 \end{array}$$

"Eight is the number
brought down.
The problems' not done.
How long
to go around?"

"**D**irty **M**onkeys **S**mell **B**ad.
'**D**' for **D**ivide.
Doing math on a pad."

"How many times
can twenty-two fit into
fourty-eight?
Let's finish up —
not much longer now
to wait.
Maybe two?
Let's see..."

$$22 \overline{)1808} \quad 8$$
$$-176$$
$$\rightarrow 48$$

"As I told you
in division scrap paper is mandatory."

$$\begin{array}{r} 22 \\ \times\ 2 \\ \hline 44 \end{array}$$

"Two is certainly enough.
Trying to fit twenty-two in a third
time would certainly
be rough!"

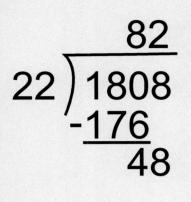

$$22 \overline{)1808}$$
$$82$$
$$-176$$
$$48$$

"'**M**' for **M**onkey
also stands for"

_____.

"That's great! Thanks for giving it a try!"

"Two times two is" _____.

$$22 \overline{)1808}$$
$$82$$
$$-176$$
$$48$$
$$4$$

"Two times two is" _____.

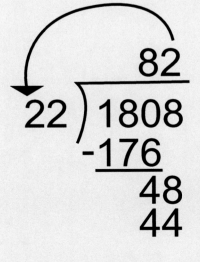

$$22 \overline{)1808}$$
$$82$$
$$-176$$
$$48$$
$$44$$

"Great! What more?"

"'**S**' for **S**mell also stands for"

_____.

```
        82
  22 ) 1808
      -176
        48
       -44
         4
```

"Fourty-eight minus
fourty-four is four.
And that's a fact!"

```
       82R4
  22 ) 1808
      -176
        48
       -44
         4
```

There's nothing left
but a remainder of four.
The way we did this problem
made it fun —
not a bore.

Now with clean monkey armpits
    fingers, and toes —
Clean monkey ears, face,
    and nose —
A clean monkey body
    and clean monkey clothes —

Make everyone happy and glad —

'Cause everyone knows

Dirty **M**onkeys **S**mell **B**ad!

| **D**IVIDE | **M**ULTIPLY | **S**UBTRACT | **B**RINGDOWN |

GLOSSARY

You understood these words in context. Go back and see if you can come up with your own definition of each. Then check the dictionary to see if you are right.

Disguising	Diabolical
Hoarse	Bore
Abide	Apparently
Illustrate	Mandatory
Logical	

ANSWER KEY

Page 15:

"'M' for Monkey also stands for" **multiply**.
"Two times two is" **four**
"Two times two is" **four**

Page 16:

"'S' for Smell also stands for" **subtract**.

Request for a Review

I sincerely hope you enjoyed using this educational tool as much as I enjoyed writing it. If you did, I would greatly appreciate a short review on Amazon or your favorite book or instructional materials website. Reviews are crucial for letting others know of the value of any instructional resource, and even just a line or two can make a huge difference.

Connect with The Author

G. Katz Chronicle has over three decades of teaching experience in primary, secondary, and higher education. Having taught all major content areas in primary and middle school, as well as education theory and biology at the secondary and college level, she most enjoys teaching the Life Sciences.

With a PhD in Curriculum and Instruction, she, too, is a perpetual student of traditional education and all areas of self-improvement.

G. Katz is an abbreviated form of Gertrude Katz. Gertrude maintains a Biology Teaching Blog where she provides her general instructional plans, reasoning, and thoughts for the NY State Living Environment Course. The blog consists of ten posts, which correspond to ten instructional units, and include unit presentations and videos. Gertrude invites you to check it out at: GertrudeKatzChronicle.com. Connect with her on other social media, as well!